Eleanor Radel

LADY CLARE.

BY

ALFRED TENNYSON.

22 ILLUSTRATIONS BY

ALFRED FREDERICKS, GRANVILLE PERKINS, FREDERIC
B. SCHELL, EDMUND H. GARRETT, F. S.
CHURCH AND HARRY FENN.

PORTER & COATES,
PHILADELPHIA.

LIST OF ILLUSTRATIONS.

ILLUSTRATIONS.

IT was the time
  when lilies blow,
    And clouds are highest up in air,

L ORD RONALD brought a lily-white
doe
To give his cousin, Lady Clare.

I TROW they did not part in
scorn:
Lovers long betrothed were
they;

They two will wed the mor-
row morn:
God's blessing on the day!

"HE does not love me for my
birth,
Nor for my lands so broad and
fair;
He loves me for my
own true
worth,
And that
is well,"
said
Lady
Clare.

IN there came old Alice
   the nurse,
Said, "Who was this
   that went from thee?"
     "It was my cousin," said Lady Clare;
     "To-morrow he weds with me."

"OH, God be thanked!" said
Alice the nurse,
"That all comes round so just
and fair:
Lord Ronald is heir of all
your lands,
And you are not
the Lady
Clare."

"ARE ye out of your mind, my nurse, my nurse,"
   Said Lady Clare, "that ye speak so wild?"
"As God's above," said Alice the nurse,
   "I speak the truth: you are my child.

"The old earl's daughter died at my breast;
   I speak the truth, as I live by bread!
I buried her like my own sweet child,
   And put my child in her stead."

"FALSELY, false-
ly have ye done,
O mother," she said, "if
this be true,
To keep the best man under
the sun
So many years from his
due."

" Nay now, my child," said Alice the nurse,
" But keep the secret for your life,
And all you have will be Lord Ronald's,
When you are man and wife."

" I F I'm a beggar born," she said,
    " I will speak out, for I dare not lie.
Pull off, pull off the brooch of gold,
    And fling the diamond necklace by."

"NAY now, my child," said Alice the nurse,
 "But keep the secret all you can."
She said, "Not so; but I will know
 If there be any faith in man."

 "Nay now, what faith?" said Alice the
  nurse,
  "The man will cleave unto his right."
 "And he shall have it," the lady re-
  plied,
  "Though I should die to-night."

" YET give one kiss to your mother, dear!
Alas, my child! I sinned for thee."
" O mother, mother, mother," she said,
"So strange it seems to me!

" Yet here's a kiss for my mother dear,
My mother dear, if this be so,
And lay your hand upon my head,
And bless me, mother, ere I go."

SHE clad herself in a russet gown,
   She was no longer Lady Clare:
She went by dale, and she went by down,
   With a single rose in her hair.

THE lily-white doe Lord Ronald had brought
    Leapt up from where she lay,
Dropped her head in the maiden's hand,
    And followed her all the way.

DOWN stepped Lord Ronald from his

    tower:

"O Lady Clare, you shame your worth!

    Why come you dressed like a vil-

    lage maid,

That are the flower of the earth?"

"IF I come dressed like a village maid,
   I am but as my fortunes are:
I am a beggar born," she said,
   "And not the Lady Clare."

"PLAY me no tricks," said Lord Ronald,
    "For I am yours in word and in deed;
Play me no tricks," said Lord Ronald,
    "Your riddle is hard to read."

OH, and proudly stood
she up!
Her heart within her
did not fail:
She looked into Lord Ronald's eyes,
And told him all her nurse's tale.

HE laughed a laugh of merry scorn:
     He turned and kissed her where she stood;
"If you are not the heiress born,
     And I," said he, "the next in blood—

" IF you are not the heiress born,
　　And I," said he, " the lawful heir,
We two will wed to-morrow morn,
　　And you shall still be Lady Clare."